PRACTICE WRITING SERIES

Let's Write — Beginners' Level
Pre-writing Activities

Written by Paula Corbett
Illustrated by Jane Shasky

TABLE OF CONTENTS

TO THE PARENT/TEACHER

The pages contained in PRE-WRITING have been planned to provide parents and teachers with a comprehensive range of activities to assist children in the development of their handwriting while making the transition from scribble to correct letter formation.

These worksheets provide practice for all the basic movements used in the format of letters — upstrokes, downward strokes, horizontal strokes, oval and others.

A popular Mother Goose theme is used with each activity page to provide additional interest for children as they complete each activity. Children should be encouraged to color, trace, or track each activity as directed to develop a free and fluent hand movement.

The practice provided by these activity pages is common for all penmanship systems and will provide a valuable foundation in the child's development of a legible style of handwriting.

Name _____

Rain, Rain, Go Away

Trace the clouds and rain.

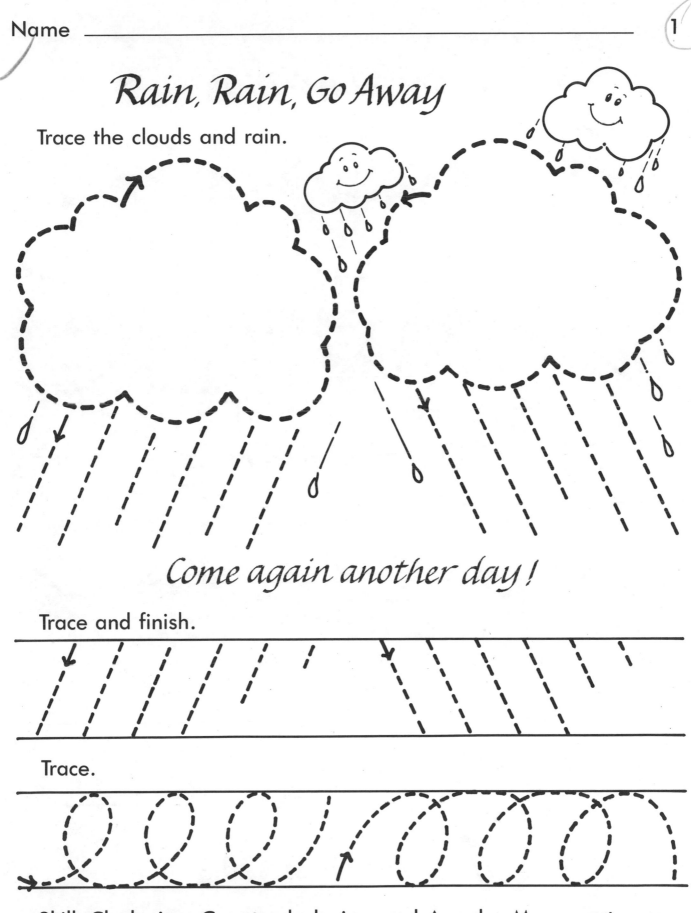

Come again another day !

Trace and finish.

Trace.

Skill: Clockwise, Counterclockwise, and Angular Movement

Rub-a-Dub-Dub

Trace the waves.

→

Three men in a tub.

Skill: Clockwise Movement

Cock-a-Doodle-Do!

Start at the arrow. Draw a line to the lost shoe. Try to keep your line midway between the lines.

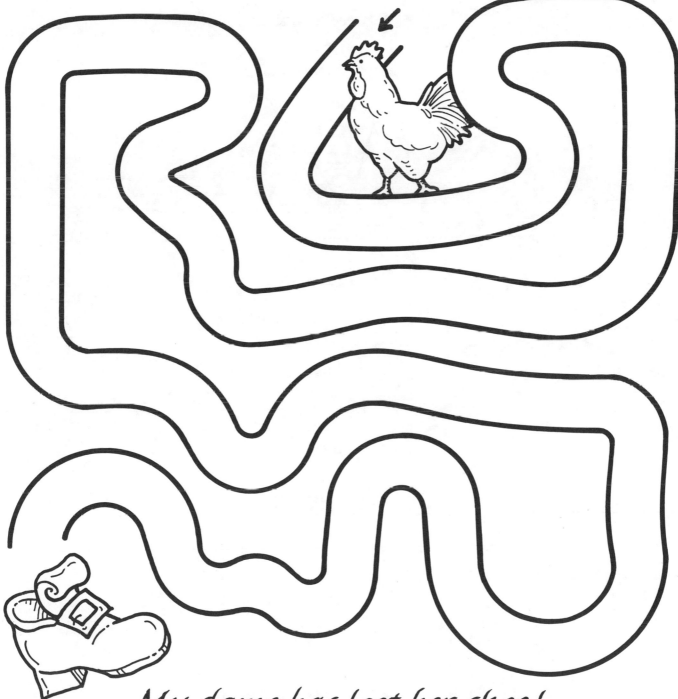

My dame has lost her shoe!

Skill: Parallel Line

NO. SE102R © COPYRIGHT, 1994, HAYES SCHOOL PUBLISHING CO., INC., PITTSBURGH, PA

Little Miss Muffet

Trace the spider's web.

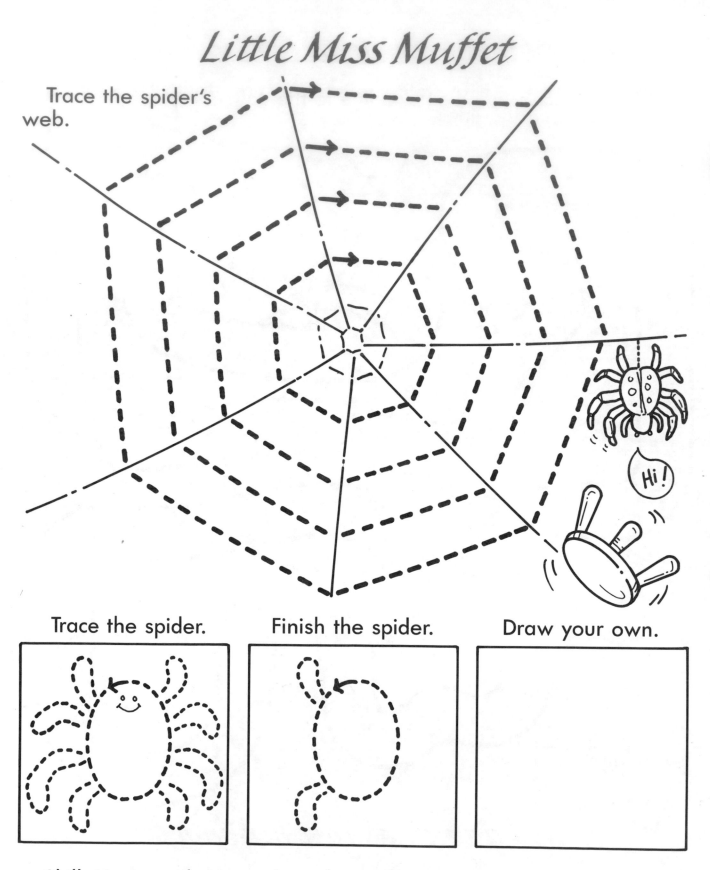

Trace the spider.   Finish the spider.   Draw your own.

Skill: Horizontal, Vertical, and Angular Movement

Where Has My Little Dog Gone?

Start at the arrow and draw a line to the dog. Try to keep your line midway between the lines.

Skill: Parallel Line

As I Was Going Along, Long, Long

Start at the arrow and trace the path along the lane. Try to keep your line midway between the lines.

The lane that I went was so long, long, long.

Skill: Parallel Line

Little Bo-Peep

Start at the arrow and draw a line to the sheep. Try to keep your line midway between the lines.

has lost her sheep!

Skill: Parallel Line

Little Bob Robin

Start at the arrow and draw a line to the robin's home. Try to keep your line midway between the lines.

Where do you live?

Skill: Parallel Line

NO. SE102R © COPYRIGHT, 1994, HAYES SCHOOL PUBLISHING CO., INC., PITTSBURGH, PA

Ten Little Bluebirds

Trace the needles
on the pine tree.

Perched on a pine.

Skill: Clockwise and Counterclockwise Movement

Hearts

Trace the key and the patterns on the hearts.

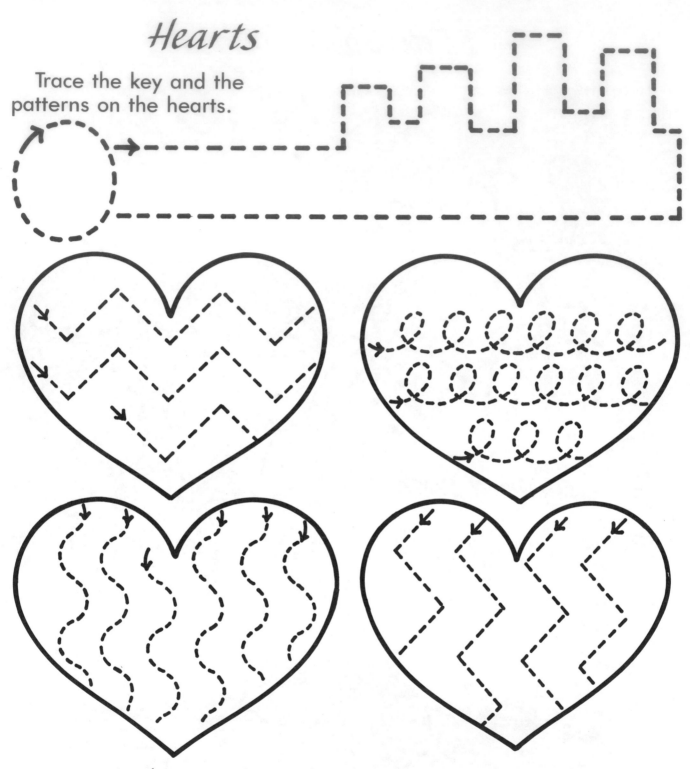

Hearts, like doors, will open with ease to very, very little keys,
And don't forget that two of these are "thank you" and "please."

Skill: Vertical, Horizontal, Angular, Clockwise, and Counterclockwise Movement

The Balloon

Trace the patterns on the balloons.

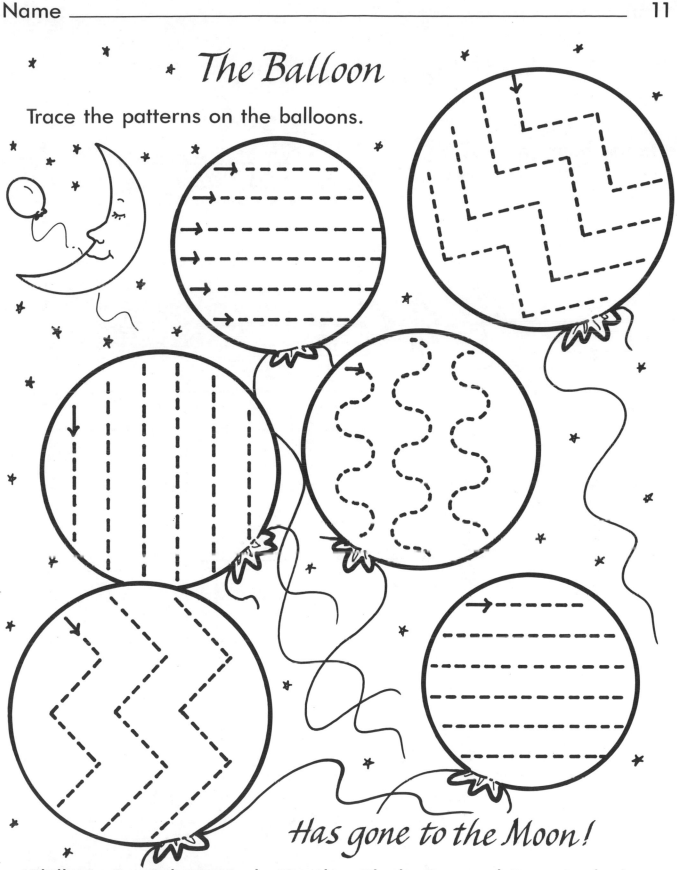

Has gone to the Moon!

Skill: Horizontal, Vertical, Angular, Clockwise, and Counterclockwise Movement

Great A, Little a

Trace the cupboard
and the bouncing B's.

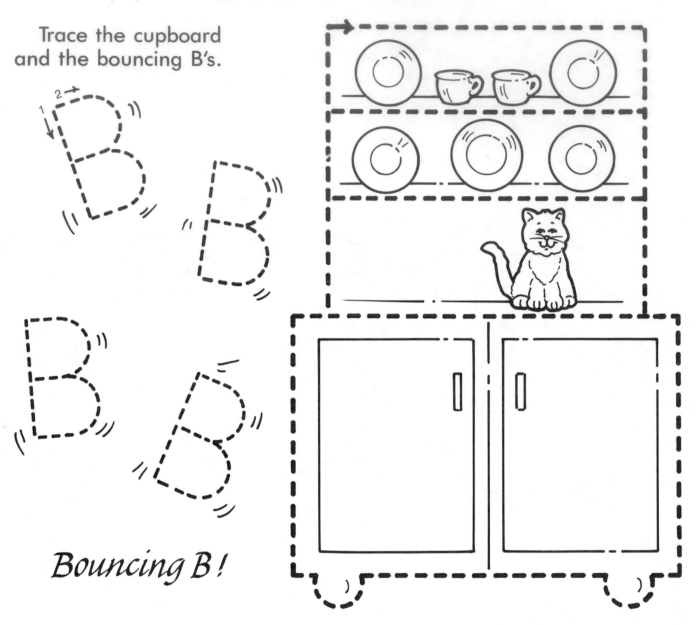

Bouncing B !

Trace the great A and little a.

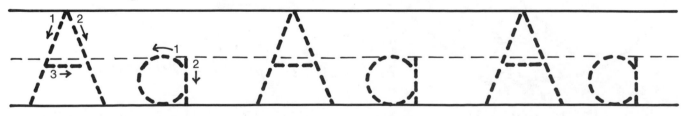

Skill: Horizontal, Vertical Movement; Uppercase A and B, Lowercase a

Handy Pandy

Trace the patterns on the candy. Draw your own.

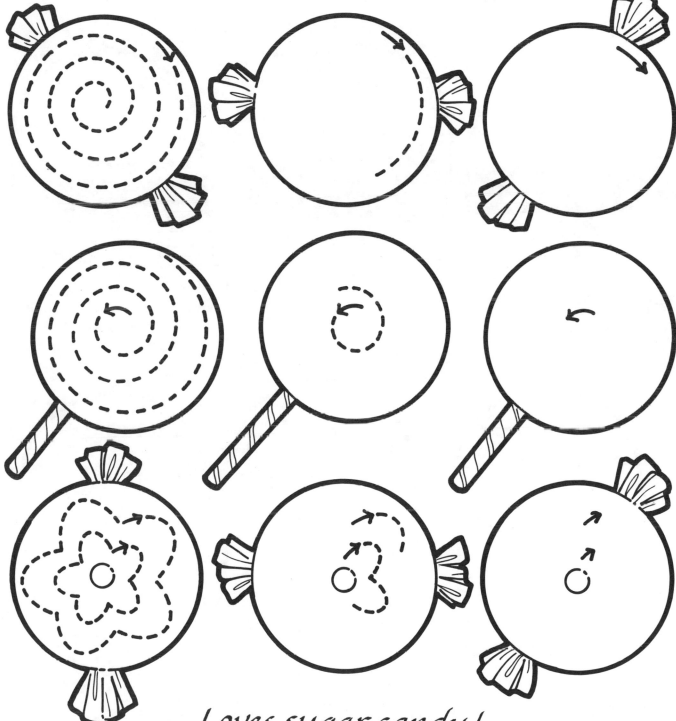

Loves sugar candy!

Skill: Clockwise and Counterclockwise Movement

Merry Are the Bells

Trace the patterns on the bells.

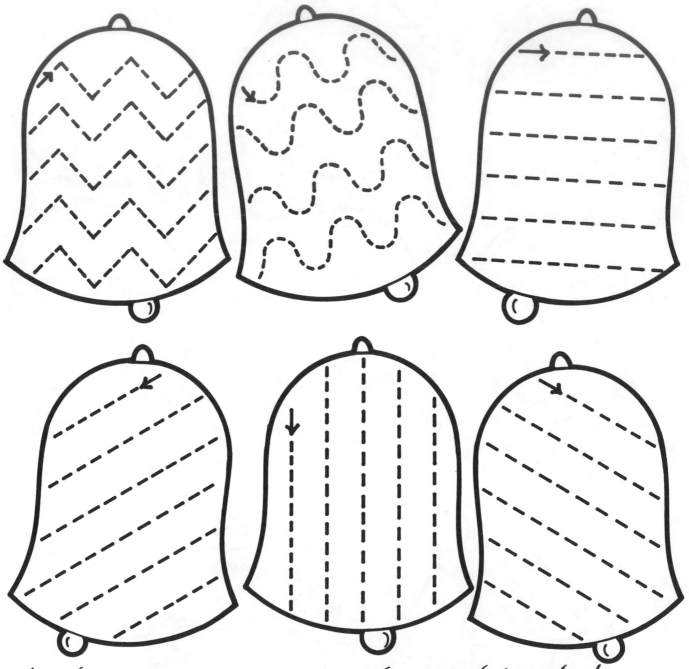

And a merry sing-song, happy let us be!

Skill: Angular, Horizontal, Vertical, Clockwise, and Counterclockwise Movement

Three Little Kittens

Trace the patterns on the mittens.

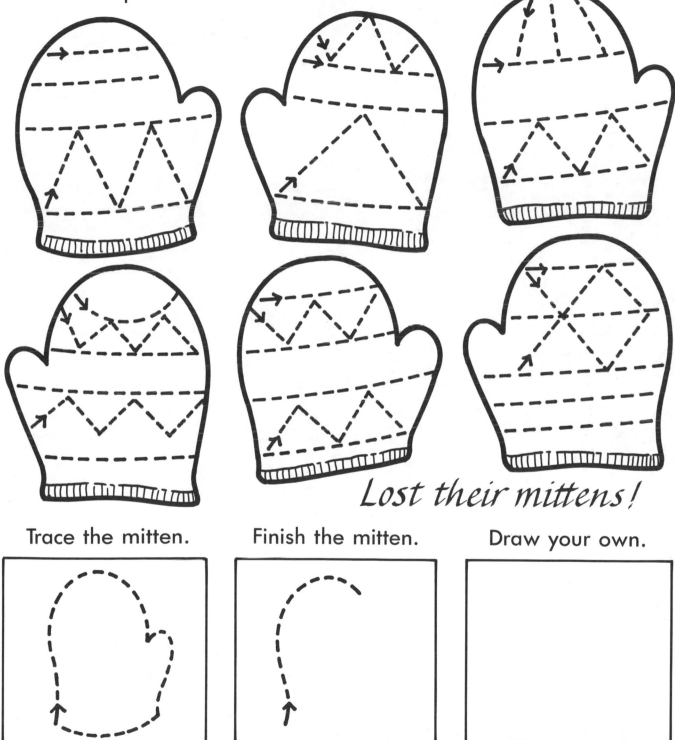

Lost their mittens!

Trace the mitten.   Finish the mitten.   Draw your own.

Skill: Horizontal, Vertical, Angular, and Counterclockwise Movement

Black Within and Red Without

Trace the chimney
and the smoke.

Four corners round about.

Skill: Clockwise, Counterclockwise, Vertical, and Angular Movement

It's Raining, It's Pouring

Trace the Z's.

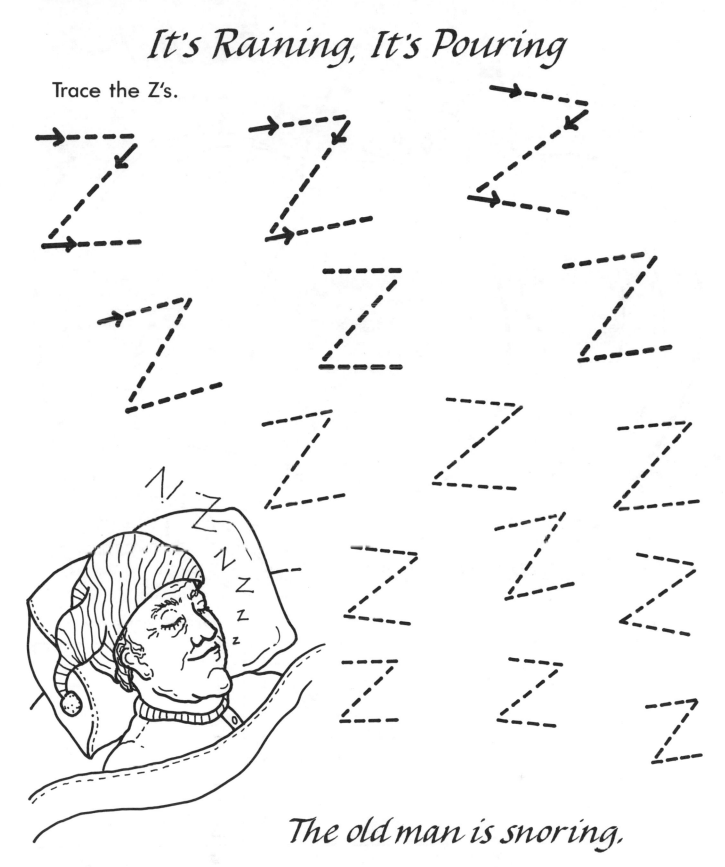

The old man is snoring.

Skill: Angular Movement

Name _____   18

Trace the bat.

Bat, Bat

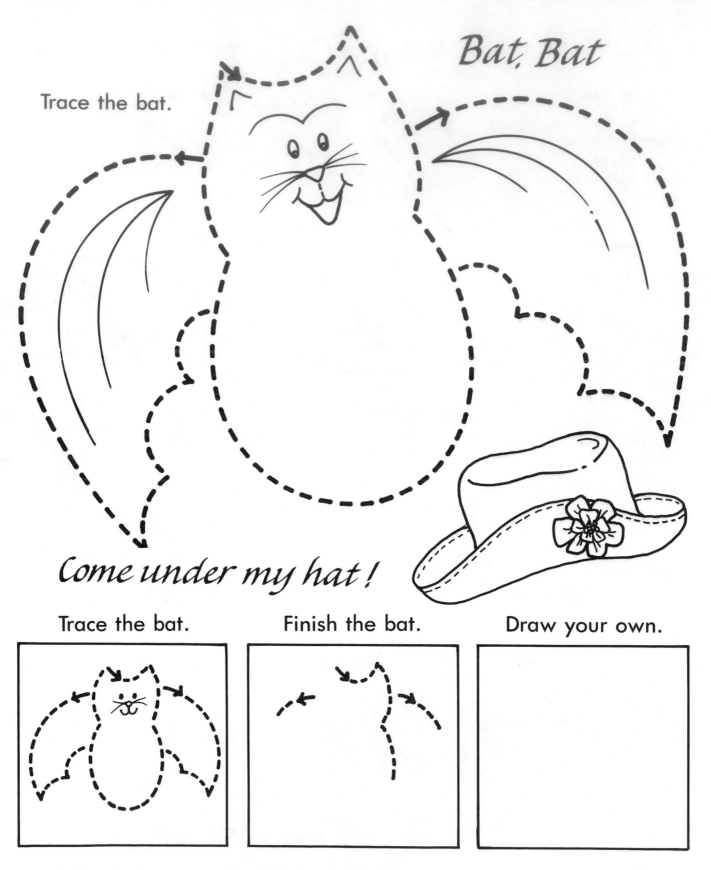

Come under my hat!

Trace the bat.   Finish the bat.   Draw your own.

Skill: Clockwise and Counterclockwise Movement

Terence McDiddler

Trace the fish and the waves.

Can charm the fish from the sea!

Trace the fish.   Finish the fish.   Draw your own.

Skill: Clockwise and Counterclockwise Movement

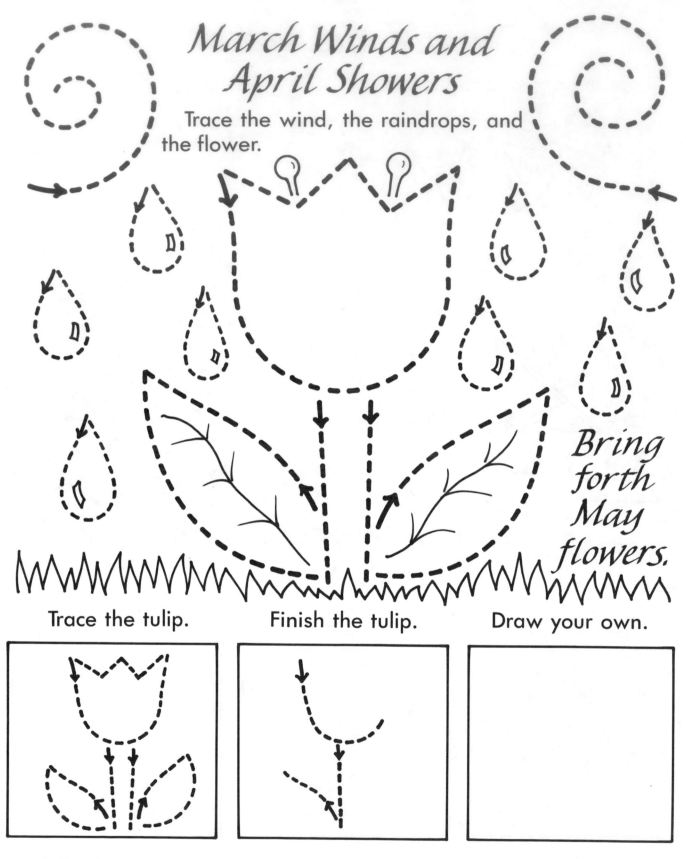

March Winds and April Showers

Trace the wind, the raindrops, and the flower.

Bring forth May flowers.

Trace the tulip.   Finish the tulip.   Draw your own.

Skill: Clockwise, Counterclockwise, Angular, and Vertical Movement

NO. SE102R © COPYRIGHT, 1994, HAYES SCHOOL PUBLISHING CO., INC., PITTSBURGH, PA

Ladybird, Ladybird

Trace the sun and the ladybug.

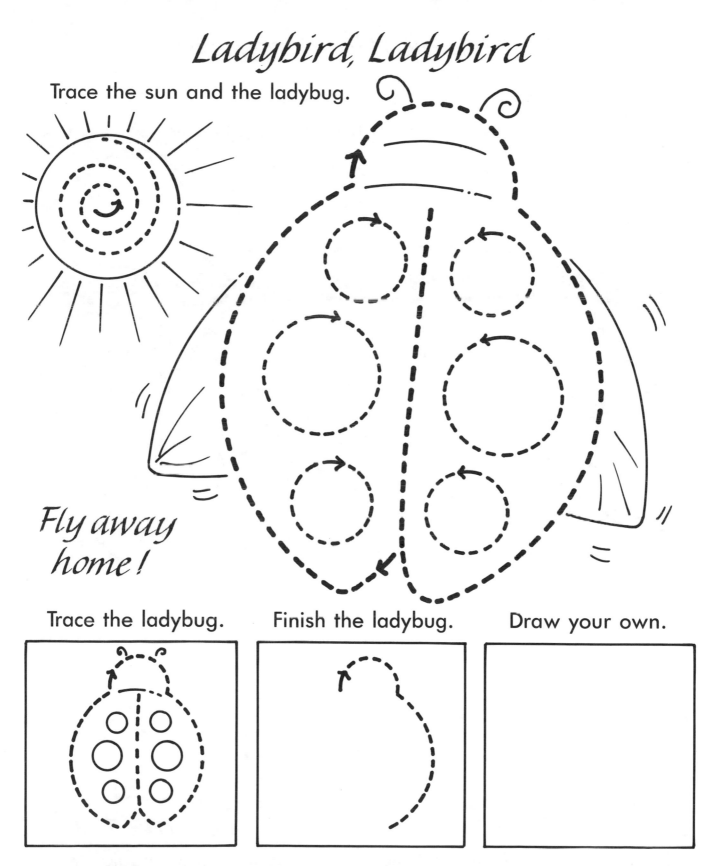

Fly away home!

Trace the ladybug. Finish the ladybug. Draw your own.

Skill: Clockwise and Counterclockwise Movement

Polly Put the Kettle On

Trace the kettle
and the steam.

We'll all have tea!

Skill: Clockwise, Counterclockwise, Horizontal, and Angular Movement

One Blue Hen

Trace the hen and the eggs.
Color them blue.

Lays blue eggs.

Skill: Clockwise and Counterclockwise Movement

Baa, Baa Black Sheep

Trace the wool on the sheep.

Have you any wool?

Skill: Clockwise and Counterclockwise Movement

Hot Cross Buns

Hot cross buns, hot cross buns, one a penny, two a penny, hot cross buns.

Trace the crosses on the buns.

Make your own crosses on the buns.

Skill: Angular Movement

Bees

Trace the behive and the paths of the bees.

Trace the bee.   Finish the bee.   Draw your own.

Skill: Clockwise, Counterclockwise, and Horizontal Movement

The Cow Jumps Over the Moon

Trace the cow and the moon.

Skill: Clockwise and Counterclockwise Movement

Green Cheese

Trace the cheese.
Color it green!

Trace.

Skill: Clockwise and Counterclockwise Movement, Uppercase and Lower Case o

Jack Be Nimble

Trace the candle and the rays.

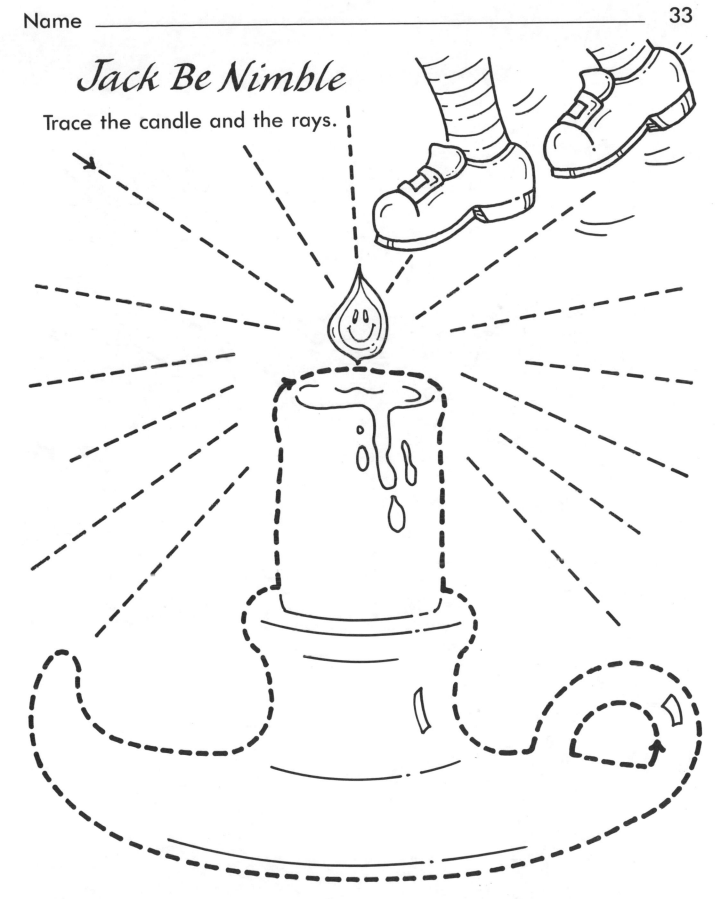

Skill: Angular, Clockwise, and Counterclockwise Movement

Snow, Snow Faster

Trace the feathers.

Skill: Angular, Clockwise, and Counterclockwise Movement

Penny and Penny

Trace the coins and the bank.

Skill: Clockwise and Counterclockwise Movement

Trace the owl and the leaves.

Fair Owl

Trace the owl.   Finish the owl.   Draw your own.

Skill: Clockwise and Counterclockwise Movement

Peter, Peter, Pumpkin Eater

Trace and color the pumpkin.

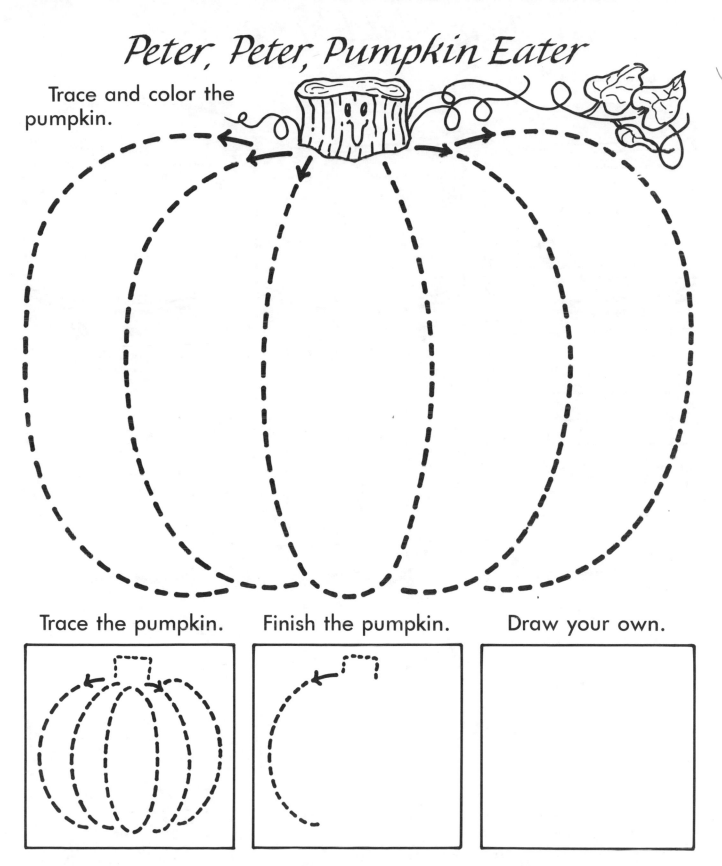

Trace the pumpkin.   Finish the pumpkin.   Draw your own.

Skill: Clockwise and Counterclockwise Movement

Bring Daddy Home

Trace the patterns.

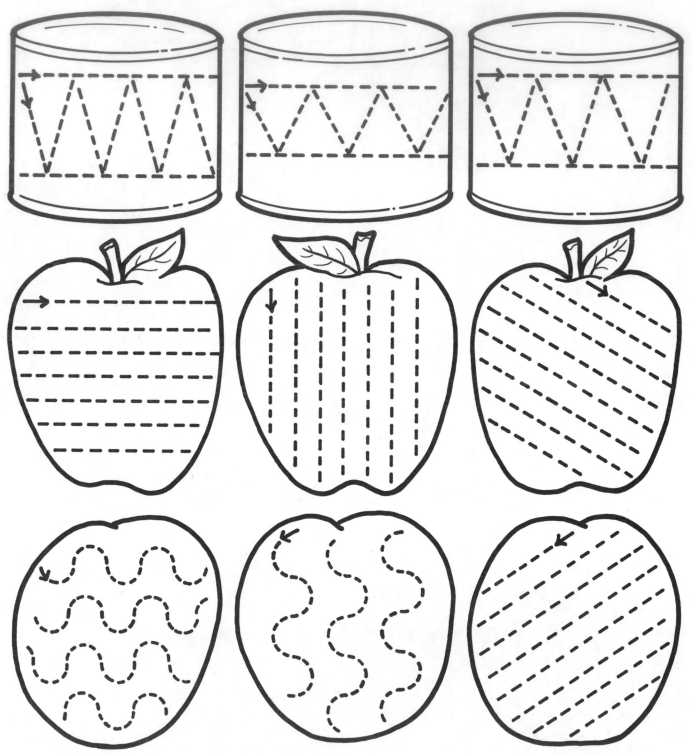

Skill: Horizontal, Vertical, Angular, Clockwise, and Counterclockwise Movement

Snails and Puppy Dog's Tails

Trace the snail and the tails.

Trace

Skill: Clockwise and Counterclockwise Movement

How Does Your Garden Grow?

Trace the garden.

Skill: Clockwise, Counterclockwise, and Vertical Movement

NO. SE102R © COPYRIGHT, 1994, HAYES SCHOOL PUBLISHING CO., INC., PITTSBURGH, PA

Pat-a-Cake

Trace.

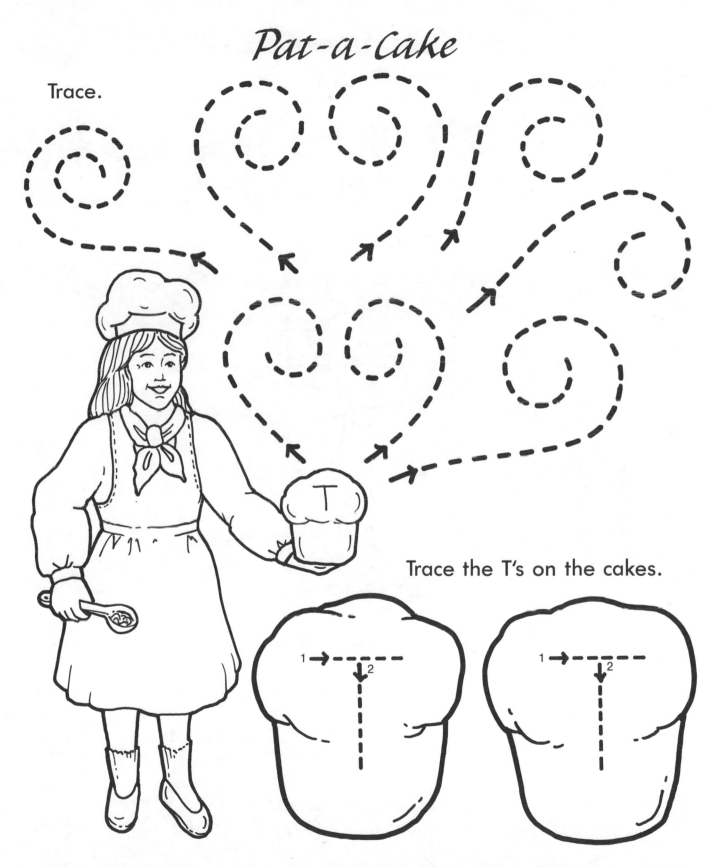

Trace the T's on the cakes.

Skill: Clockwise and Counterclockwise Movement and Uppercase T

NO. SE102R © COPYRIGHT, 1994, HAYES SCHOOL PUBLISHING CO., INC., PITTSBURGH, PA

Old Farmer Giles

Trace the picture.

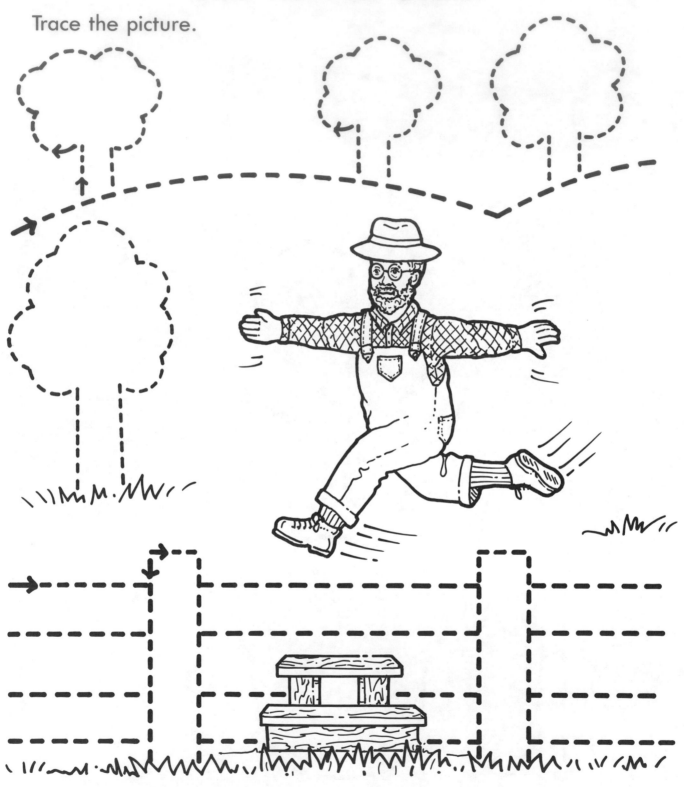

Skill: Horizontal, Vertical, and Clockwise Movement

Needle and Thread

Trace the thread pattern.

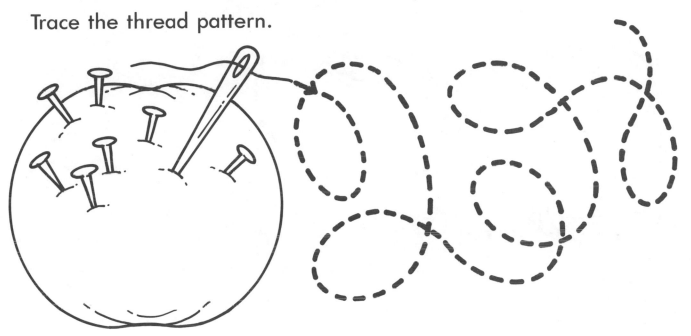

Draw your own patterns.

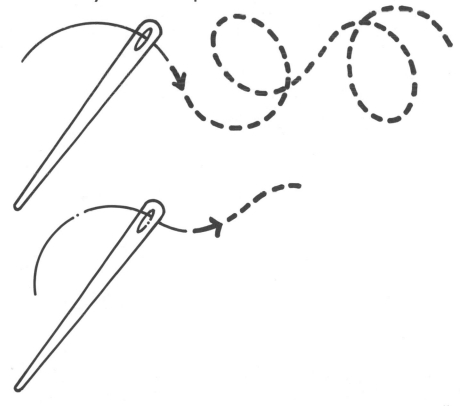

Skill: Clockwise and Counterclockwise Movement

Hickory, Dickory Dock

Trace the paths of the mice.

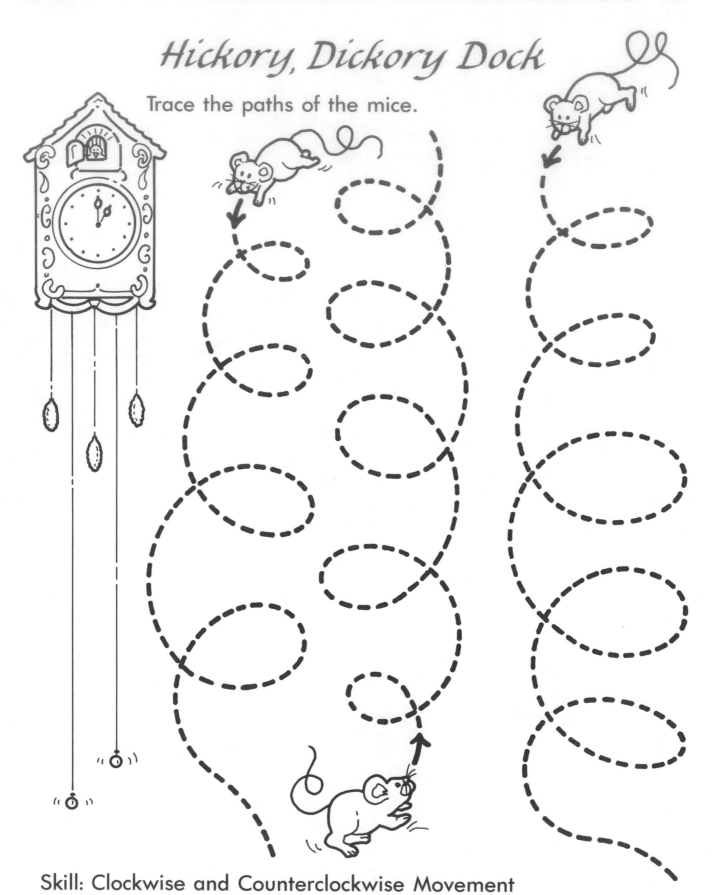

Skill: Clockwise and Counterclockwise Movement

Little Jack Pumpkin Face

Trace the vines.

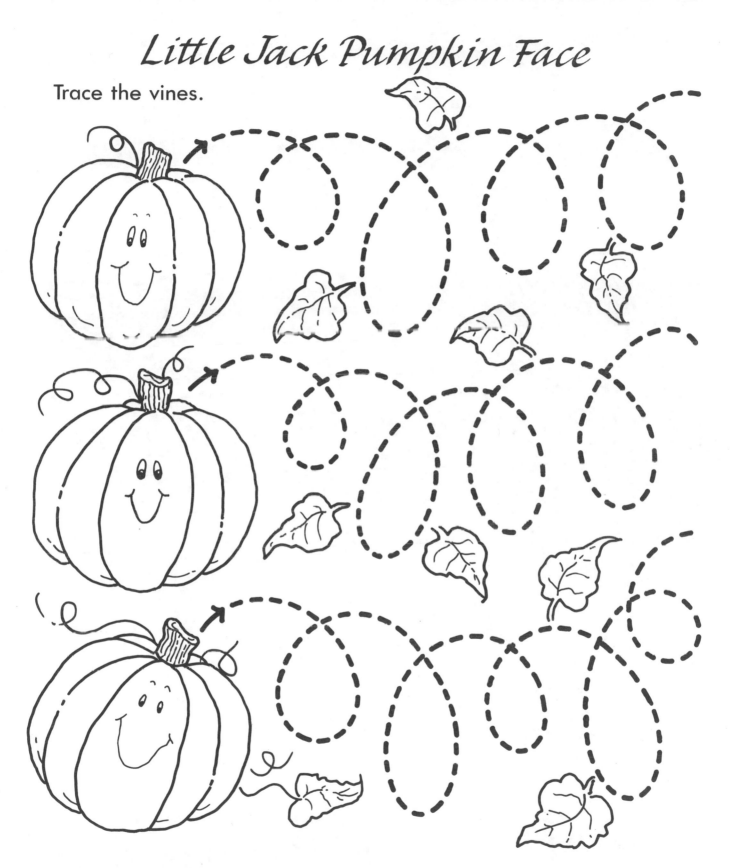

Skill: Clockwise Movement

Sing, Sing, What Shall I Sing?

Trace the string.

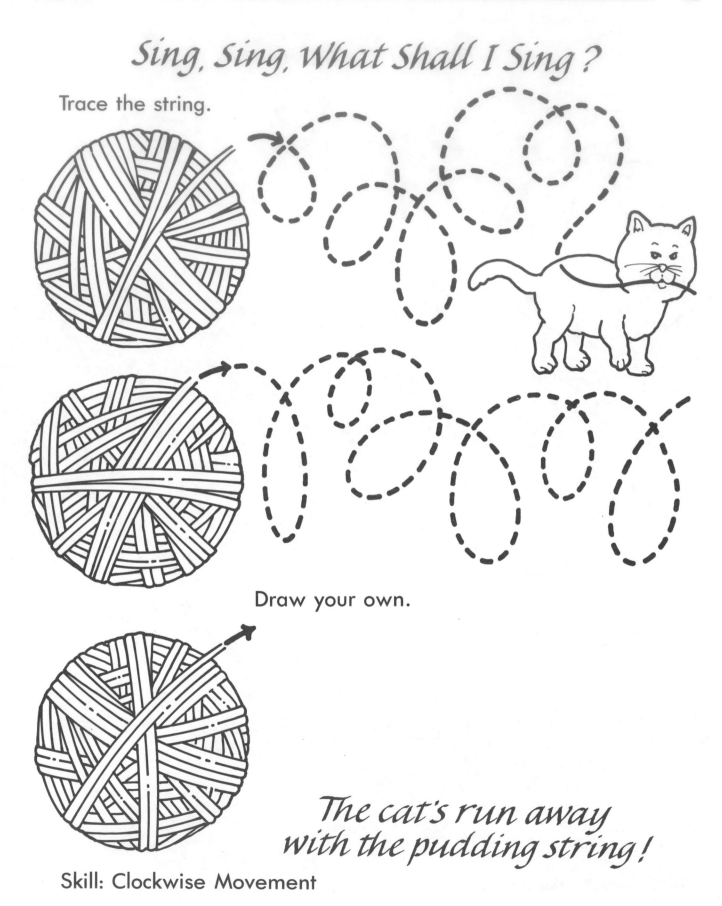

Draw your own.

*The cat's run away
with the pudding string!*

Skill: Clockwise Movement

NO. SE102R © COPYRIGHT, 1994, HAYES SCHOOL PUBLISHING CO., INC., PITTSBURGH, PA

Humpty Dumpty

Trace Humpty Dumpty's path.

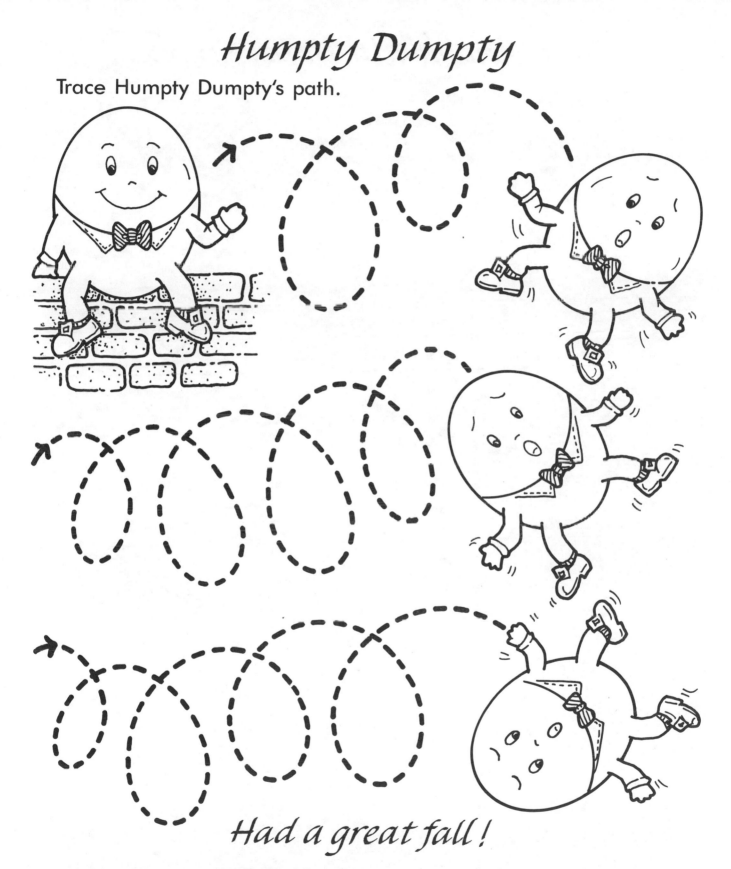

Had a great fall!

Skill: Clockwise Movement

NO. SE102R © COPYRIGHT, 1994, HAYES SCHOOL PUBLISHING CO., INC., PITTSBURGH, PA

Hobbledy Hops

Trace the paths of the tops.

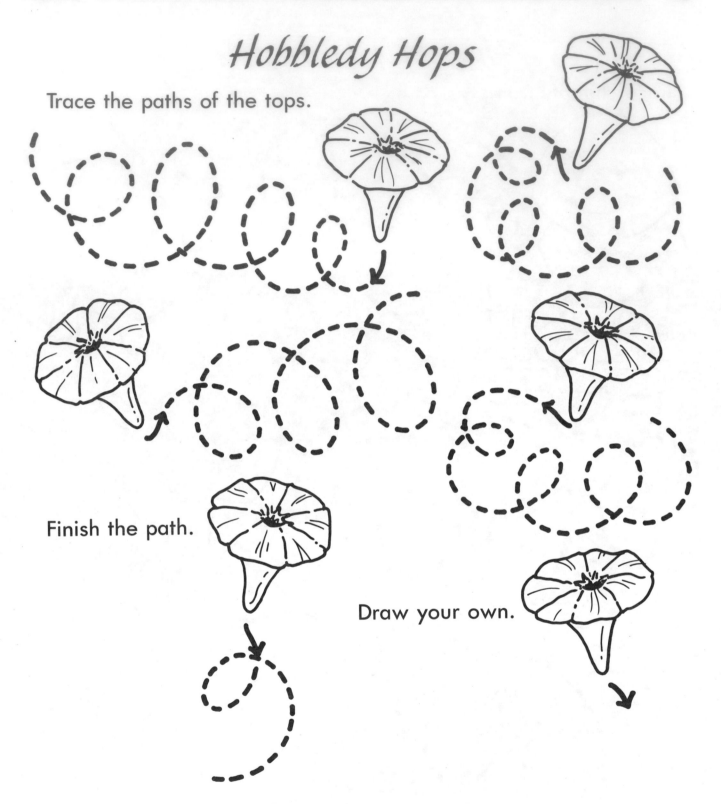

Finish the path.

Draw your own.

He made some tops out of the morning glory.

Skill: Clockwise and Counterclockwise Movement

NO. SE102R © COPYRIGHT, 1994, HAYES SCHOOL PUBLISHING CO., INC., PITTSBURGH, PA